Core Knowledge Language Arts®

Zack and Ann
Unit 9 Reader

Skills Strand
KINDERGARTEN

Amplify learning.

Core Knowledge®

ISBN 978-1-61700-156-7

Printed in the USA
07 LSCOW 2021

Table of Contents
Zack and Ann
Unit 9 Reader

Pausing Point (Stories for Assessment and Enrichment)

The Bad Crab

This is Zack Chang.

Zack is six.

3

This is Ann Chang.

Ann is ten.

Zack and Ann sit in the sun.

Mom and Dad sit with them.

Zack spots a crab on the sand.

The crab runs up.

Then it snaps at Zack's leg.

Zack jumps up on the bench.

The bad crab snaps at Dad.

Dad lifts up his legs.

The bad crab snaps at Mom.

Mom kicks sand at the crab.

The bad crab runs off.

Ann jumps up and yells

at the kids on the next bench,

"Bad crab on the sand!

Pass the word!"

The kids on the next bench

spot the crab and jump up.

The bad crab snaps at them.

Then it runs past them.

<u>Wh</u>en it is past them, the kids

yell,

"Bad crab on the sand!

Pass the w<u>or</u>d!"

Ann's Dress

Ann went to Gwen's Dress

Shop.

The shop had a red dress.

Ann got the dress.

Ann got in a cab with the dress.

The cab man sped off.

His cab went fast.

Then the cab hit a big bump.

Thump!

Ann's dress fell from the cab.

Ann had the cab man stop the
cab.

Then Ann ran back to get the
dress.

Ann had to run ten blocks.

Ann's dress w<u>a</u>s in a trash can.

A bus had hit it.

A dog bit it.

The dress had mud on it.

The dress had rips and missing

bits.

Ann's dress w<u>a</u>s a mess!

Zack Gets a Pet

"Can <u>I</u> get a cat?" Zack asks.

Dad tells Zack, "N<u>o</u> cats!

Cats run up trees and can't get

back."

"Can I get a rat?" Zack asks.

Mom adds, "No, no! No rats!"

"Rats smell bad."

"Can I get a bug?" Zack asks.

Ann tells Zack, "No, no! A bug is

not a pet!"

"Can I get a fish?" Zack asks.

"A fish?" his mom asks.

"A fish is not s<u>o</u> bad.

Can a fish be a fun pet?"

Dad nods and Ann shrugs.

"Can <u>I</u> get <u>one</u>, then?" Zack

asks.

Mom nods.

"Yes!" yells Zack.

Zack runs to the pet shop.

"Can I get that fish?" Zack asks.

"This one?" the pet shop man asks.

Zack nods.

"This one costs six bucks."

Zack hands the man the cash.

Then Zack runs to Mom and Dad with his pet fish.

29

On the Mat

Zack and Ann had fun on a mat.

Zack got on the mat.

Then Ann got on next t<u>o</u> Zack.

Then Quinn got on next t<u>o</u> Ann.

Nell got up on top of Zack and Ann.

Rod got up on top of Ann and Quinn.

Then Ed got up on the tip top.

It was so much fun!

Then, buzz, buzz!

What was that?

It was a bug.

The bug was on Zack's chin.

Zack went to smack the bug.

35

Flop!

Zack fell flat on the mat.

Nell fell on top of Zack.

Then all the rest of the kids fell.

It was a big mess.

Fix That Ship

Zack's dad, Dan, has a ship.

It's fun to fish on the ship.

But Dan can't fish on the ship yet.

Dan must fix up his ship.

The ship has a big crack in its mast.

It has dents which Dan must fix.

It has rust which Dan must sand.

38

Dan gets the ship up on the land.

Then Dan gets a mask.

The mask will help block the dust.

Dan sands the deck.

Dan rubs and scrubs.

Dan drills and bangs.

At last, Dan's ship is _all_ set.

The Tent

<u>Once</u> Zack's dad got the kids a tent.

Zack and Ann set up the tent.

Then the kids sang a song:

"This big tent, it is the best,

is the best, is the best!

This big tent, it is the best.

Yes, it's the best!"

The kids had fun in the tent.

But then a big wind hit the tent.

Flop!

The tent fell on Zack and Ann.

Then Zack felt a drip.

Drip, drop, drip, drop.

Splish, splash, splish, splash.

Zack and Ann got wet.

The kids set the tent back up.

47

Red ants got in and bit Zack.

A slug got on Ann.

<u>Once</u> the ants and slug got in,

that w<u>a</u>s it.

Zack and Ann ran fr<u>o</u>m the

tent.

A Gift from Mom

Once Mom got the kids a gift.

The gift was in a big black box.

Mom set the box on the rug.

"Is it a truck?" Zack said.

"No," Mom said. "It's not a

truck."

"I bet it's a hat," Ann said.

"No," Mom said. "It's not a hat."

Then the box said, "Ruff, ruff!"

Zack slid the lid off the box.

A dog sat up.

"It's a dog!" said Ann.

"Yes!" said Zack.

"Mom's the best!"

Bug and Frog

Zack and Ann sit next to the pond.

Zack says, "The pond is a lot of fun! I wish I were a bug."

"Why?" says Ann. "Bugs are no fun."

"Bugs zip and hum" says Zack.

"Frogs hop and splash and munch on bugs," says Ann.

"I will not wish I was a bug." Zack quips.

Zack and Ann had fun at the pond. They will tell Mom and Dad.

Swing That Net

Zack is at the pond.

There are lots of frogs in the pond.

Zack runs in to get one.

But the frogs are so quick!

The frogs are so slick!

When Zack runs in,

the frogs hop off.

Zack gets a net and runs in.

The frogs all jump.

Zack swings his net and yells,

"Get in here, frogs!"

Swish!

Zack gets a frog in his net!

Zack yells and swings the net.

Swish, swish, swish!

Swish, swish, swish!

Zack gets lots <u>of</u> frogs.

Th<u>ere</u> <u>are</u> six big <u>ones</u> in his

net!

Spot's Bath

Spot is in his bathtub.

Spot and his dog pals went

in a mud pit.

The kids must get the mud off.

Spot is <u>one</u> sad dog.

His dog pals <u>are</u> still in the mud

pit.

But Spot is stuck in the tub.

Zack grips Spot with his hands.

Then his hands slip.

Spot runs off.

The kids run to the mud pit.

There's Spot, back in the mud

with the rest of his dog pals.

"Spot!" Zack yells. "Bad dog!"

"Spot!" Ann yells.

"Get back in that tub!"

The Pots and Pans Band

Zack and Ann <u>are</u> in a band.

It's a pots and pans band.

Zack and Quinn bang on pots.

Ann and Nell bang on pans.

Bang, bang! Ding, ding!

Mom wants to sing songs.

"Stop!" Mom says.

Mom asks the band to sing not

bang.

69

Mom sets up snacks and says,

"Snacks!"

The kids drop the pots and

pans and run t*o* get the snacks.

Mom grabs the pots and pans

and sets them on a shelf.

And that is the end of the

pots and pans band!

When It's Hot

When it's hot, it's fun to golf.

Zack's dad swings his golf club.

Thwack!

Zack runs up the hill.

"Where did it land?" his dad

asks.

"It's up here!" Zack yells back.

When it's hot, it's fun to fish.

Zack sits on a rock and casts.

His dad sits next to him.

"Where are all the fish?" Zack

asks.

"I can't tell," says his dad,

"but it's fun just to sit in the

sun."

When it's hot, it's fun to grill.

Zack's dad gets the hot dogs.

Zack gets the buns.

Zack's dad flips the hot dogs.

Zack sets a hot dog on a bun.

Yum, yum!

Ann's Hat Box

Ann sets a box of hats on the bed.

"Which hat is the best?" Ann asks.

"Is this black top hat the best?"

"No!" Zack says.

"That one has a big dent!"

"Is this <u>one</u> the best?" asks Ann.

"N<u>o</u>," s<u>ay</u>s Zack.

"That's a nap cap!"

"Is this <u>one</u> the best?" asks Ann.

"N<u>o</u>," s<u>ay</u>s Zack.

"This <u>one</u>?" Ann asks.

"Yuck!" s<u>ay</u>s Zack.

Ann picks lots of hats.

Zack s<u>a</u>ys n<u>o</u> t<u>o</u> <u>a</u>ll of them.

Then Ann picks a red hat.

"Is this <u>one</u> the best?" Ann asks.

"Yes!" Zack s<u>a</u>ys.

"That red hat is the best!"

Dan the Cab Man

Zack's dad, Dan, has a cab.

A man jumps in the cab.

"Where to?" Dan asks.

"Tenth and Hill," says the man.

"And step on it!" the man adds.

"I'm in a big rush!"

Dan nods and steps on the gas.

Dan zips past a van.

Dan zips past a bus.

In a flash, the cab is there.

"This is the spot!" says Dan.

The man grabs a bunch of

cash and hands it to Dan.

Help from Pals

Ann has a lot of tasks.

"Cut the grass!" says Dad.

"Scrub the pots!" says Mom.

"Trim the shrubs," says Dad.

"Brush the dog!" says Mom.

"Ug!" says Ann.

"What a lot of tasks!"

Ann asks Zack t<u>o</u> help with the tasks.

Zack runs and gets Rod and Ed.

Ann cuts the grass.

Zack and Ed scrub the pots.

Ann trims the shrubs.

Rod scrubs the dog.

Then th<u>ere</u> <u>are</u> n<u>o</u> tasks left!

Ann's Cut

Ann has a cut on <u>one</u> leg.

It's not just a cut.

It's a red gash.

"Mom!" Ann yells. "Dad!"

Mom and Dad run up.

Mom gets a pad to scrub the cut.

"No!" yells Ann. "That will sting!"

"It will sting," says Dad,

"but it will help."

Mom rubs the cut with the pad.

"It stings! It stings!" yells Ann.

"There!" Mom says. "All set!"

Ann gets a kiss from Dad

and a big hug from Mom.

About this Book

This book has been created for use by students learning to read with the Core Knowledge Reading Program. Readability levels are suitable for early readers. The book has also been carefully leveled in terms of its "code load," or the number of spellings used in the stories.

The English writing system is complex. It uses more than 200 spellings to stand for 40-odd sounds. Many sounds can be spelled several different ways, and many spellings can be pronounced several different ways. This book has been designed to make early reading experiences simpler and more productive by using a subset of the available spellings. It uses *only* spellings students have been taught to sound out as part of their phonics lessons, plus a handful of tricky words, which have also been deliberately introduced in the lessons. This means the stories will be 100% decodable if they are assigned at the proper time.

As the students move through the program, they learn new spellings and the "code load" in the decodable readers increases gradually. The code load graphic on this page indicates the number of spellings students are expected to know in order to read the first story of the book and the number of spellings students are expected to know in order to read the final stories in the book. The columns on the opposite page list the specific spellings and Tricky Words students are expected to recognize at the beginning of this reader. The bullets at the bottom of the opposite page identify spellings, tricky words, and other topics that are introduced gradually in the unit this reader accompanies.

Visit us on the web at www.coreknowledge.org

CORE KNOWLEDGE LANGUAGE ARTS

SERIES EDITOR-IN-CHIEF
E. D. Hirsch, Jr.

PRESIDENT
Linda Bevilacqua

EDITORIAL STAFF
Carolyn Gosse, Senior Editor - Preschool
Khara Turnbull, Materials Development Manager
Michelle L. Warner, Senior Editor - Listening & Learning

Mick Anderson
Robin Blackshire
Maggie Buchanan
Paula Coyner
Sue Fulton
Sara Hunt
Erin Kist
Robin Luecke
Rosie McCormick
Cynthia Peng
Liz Pettit
Ellen Sadler
Deborah Samley
Diane Auger Smith
Sarah Zelinke

DESIGN AND GRAPHICS STAFF
Scott Ritchie, Creative Director

Kim Berrall
Michael Donegan
Liza Greene
Matt Leech
Bridget Moriarty
Lauren Pack

CONSULTING PROJECT MANAGEMENT SERVICES
ScribeConcepts.com

ADDITIONAL CONSULTING SERVICES
Ang Blanchette
Dorrit Green
Carolyn Pinkerton

ACKNOWLEDGMENTS

These materials are the result of the work, advice, and encouragement of numerous individuals over many years. Some of those singled out here already know the depth of our gratitude; others may be surprised to find themselves thanked publicly for help they gave quietly and generously for the sake of the enterprise alone. To helpers named and unnamed we are deeply grateful.

CONTRIBUTORS TO EARLIER VERSIONS OF THESE MATERIALS
Susan B. Albaugh, Kazuko Ashizawa, Nancy Braier, Kathryn M. Cummings, Michelle De Groot, Diana Espinal, Mary E. Forbes, Michael L. Ford, Ted Hirsch, Danielle Knecht, James K. Lee, Diane Henry Leipzig, Martha G. Mack, Liana Mahoney, Isabel McLean, Steve Morrison, Juliane K. Munson, Elizabeth B. Rasmussen, Laura Tortorelli, Rachael L. Shaw, Sivan B. Sherman, Miriam E. Vidaver, Catherine S. Whittington, Jeannette A. Williams

We would like to extend special recognition to Program Directors Matthew Davis and Souzanne Wright who were instrumental to the early development of this program.

SCHOOLS
We are truly grateful to the teachers, students, and administrators of the following schools for their willingness to field test these materials and for their invaluable advice: Capitol View Elementary, Challenge Foundation Academy (IN), Community Academy Public Charter School, Lake Lure Classical Academy, Lepanto Elementary School, New Holland Core Knowledge Academy, Paramount School of Excellence, Pioneer Challenge Foundation Academy, New York City PS 26R (The Carteret School), PS 30X (Wilton School), PS 50X (Clara Barton School), PS 96Q, PS 102X (Joseph O. Loretan), PS 104Q (The Bays Water), PS 214K (Michael Friedsam), PS 223Q (Lyndon B. Johnson School), PS 308K (Clara Cardwell), PS 333Q (Goldie Maple Academy), Sequoyah Elementary School, South Shore Charter Public School, Spartanburg Charter School, Steed Elementary School, Thomas Jefferson Classical Academy, Three Oaks Elementary, West Manor Elementary.

And a special thanks to the CKLA Pilot Coordinators Anita Henderson, Yasmin Lugo-Hernandez, and Susan Smith, whose suggestions and day-to-day support to teachers using these materials in their classrooms was critical.

WRITERS
Matt Davis, Core Knowledge Staff

ILLUSTRATORS AND IMAGE SOURCES
All illustrations by Michael Parker